This Book Belongs To...

Piper Macdougall

birthday cake

yum!

poster paints

Hi Everyone!

When I was young I loved getting the *Girl* Annual as a special treat every year. I had *Girl* comic each week and read it eagerly from cover to cover — but I think I enjoyed the Annual even more. It seemed to be jam-packed with all my favourite stories and features, with all kinds of extra treats and surprises.

I've tried very hard to make my Annual full of treasures too. Whether you're reading it in the garden at the tail end of the summer holidays, hunched up in bed after a hard day at school, or lolling on the sofa after an enormous Christmas dinner, I hope you enjoy every single page.

Love from

Jacqueline Wilson

xxx

My three favourite pages in this annual were

1. ....

2. ....

3. ....

I'm so lucky to be a published writer. I've wanted to be an author ever since I was six years old. I've written very nearly a hundred books, but it's still thrilling when an idea pops into my head, and I realise I can write yet another new one. I love daydreaming about the story, making the characters real inside my head. It's exciting starting that first page — and even better writing *The End* many months later.

I write all my stories by hand in notebooks. I find it pretty tedious typing them all out and rewriting all the clunky bits. I'm lucky though that I hardly ever suffer from writer's block. I don't know exactly how I get my ideas — they seem to occur to me when I'm least expecting inspiration. I just try to keep an open mind, and whenever I think of something I write it down quickly so I don't forget it!

The best idea I've ever had was wondering what it would be like to be advertised if you lived in a children's home. I thought you'd have to be pretty tough to deal with the whole process — and almost at once Tracy Beaker popped into my head, fully-formed.

I've had so many wonderful things happen to me because I'm a writer. I've met the Queen and several Prime Ministers, I've had breakfast in the White House in America, I've travelled all over the world on book tours, I've won awards — but best of all, I've had many thousands of children tell me that they enjoy my books.

Maddie & Ellie meet Jacky.

Want to be just like Jacky? Turn over for lots of story writing tips and games!

5

Be An Awesome Author!

Monday

Get Comfortable!
Find somewhere comfortable to write. It could be a desk, in bed, with lots of background noise or in complete silence — whatever works best for you! The more comfortable you are, the more focused you'll be on writing.

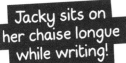
Jacky sits on her chaise longue while writing!

Tuesday

Get Inspired!
You need a topic to write about, so find something that inspires you. It might be something personal, something you've dreamt up or a beautiful picture you've seen. To get started, jot down a few sentences about the story.

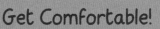
Lily Alone was inspired by my walks in Richmond Park!

Wednesday

Plan Your Plot!
Write an outline of your story and who your characters are. This plan will keep you on track if you lose focus!

Thursday

Set The Scene!
Now that you've got a story, think about where it's set. It might be a busy, bustling market, an old library or in a boarding school. Write about your setting here —

_____
_____
_____
_____

Friday

Get In Character!

Think about what you like about the books you read — not only is the story important, but the characters are too. Now imagine your character. What are their personality traits? What do they look like? What are their family like? Describe your character in five words

_____

_____

_____

_____

_____

Saturday

Time Yourself!

Challenge yourself to write for a set period of time — it can be five minutes or an hour, it's up to you! Do this regularly and you'll soon get into a writing habit. Don't be disheartened if you only manage to write a sentence — it will come in time.

Jacky writes before breakfast every day!

Sunday

Re-write!

When you've finished your story, it might be jumbled up or contain spelling and grammar mistakes. Re-write your story so that it's neat and makes sense to the reader.

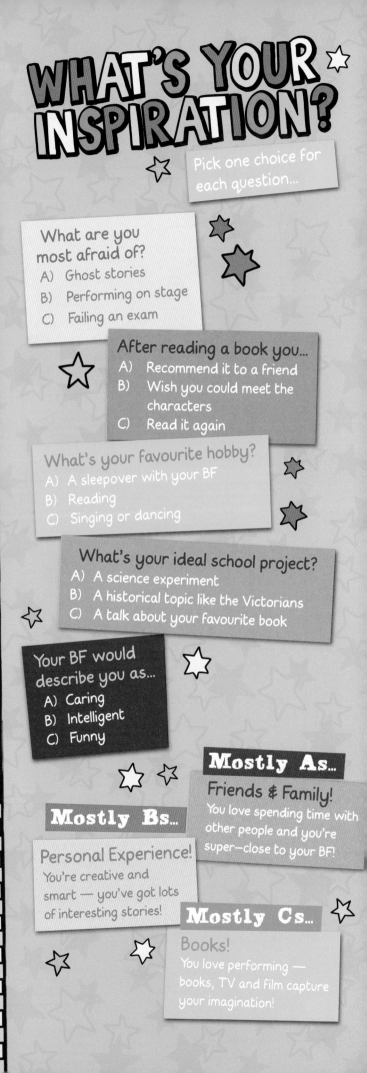

WHAT'S YOUR INSPIRATION?

Pick one choice for each question...

What are you most afraid of?
A) Ghost stories
B) Performing on stage
C) Failing an exam

After reading a book you...
A) Recommend it to a friend
B) Wish you could meet the characters
C) Read it again

What's your favourite hobby?
A) A sleepover with your BF
B) Reading
C) Singing or dancing

What's your ideal school project?
A) A science experiment
B) A historical topic like the Victorians
C) A talk about your favourite book

Your BF would describe you as...
A) Caring
B) Intelligent
C) Funny

Mostly As...
Friends & Family!
You love spending time with other people and you're super-close to your BF!

Mostly Bs...
Personal Experience!
You're creative and smart — you've got lots of interesting stories!

Mostly Cs...
Books!
You love performing — books, TV and film capture your imagination!

Charlie & Lottie's

Start by choosing your main character:

☐ Lady Louisa Butterworth

☐ A poor Foundling orphan

☐ Nanny Betsy

☐ Queen Victoria

Roll a dice to find your setting.

1. THE FOUNDLING HOSPITAL.

2. QUEEN VICTORIA'S PALACE.

3. A DRAUGHTY ATTIC ROOM.

4. AN IMPOSING VICTORIAN MANSION.

5. THE BUSTLING COBBLED STREETS.

6. A VICTORIAN CLASSROOM.

Choose your favourite colour to pick a scenario for your character to deal with.

A POCKET-WATCH MYSTERIOUSLY DISAPPEARS...

A WELL-DRESSED GENTLEMAN ARRIVES WITH LIFE-CHANGING NEWS.

AN IMPORTANT LETTER IS HAND-DELIVERED BY A RAGGED STREET BOY.

AN INFESTATION OF RATS CAUSES GREAT DISMAY!

A STREET PARTY IS ORGANISED IN HONOUR OF THE QUEEN'S BIRTHDAY.

THERE IS A TERRIBLE ACCIDENT WHEN A HORSE BREAKS AWAY FROM ITS CARRIAGE...

Story Starter

Here are some tips to help you write a realistic Victorian story:

Give your characters traditional Victorian names!

The Victorians were great fans of flowery names, such as 'Lily' or 'Rose'. Choose your characters' names carefully... a servant girl named 'Chantelle' or 'Demi' in Victorian times would be extremely unlikely!

Now start your story! Will you write about a poor little maid like me?

Use lots of descriptive words to bring your characters to life.

Think about how your character would dress, talk and walk. A wealthy Victorian lady, for instance, would wear beautiful dresses made from the finest fabrics. She'd probably appear very stiff and proper when she walked. A lady would also talk quite differently compared to a scullery maid!

What Happens NEXT?

Ever wondered what might have happened to the characters when you finish a book?

Jacqueline Wilson
The Lottie Project
Illustrated by Nick Sharratt

Have a go at continuing Charlie and Lottie's story... you can write it your way!

Here are a few questions to get you thinking:

♥ Will Jo and Mark ever get married? Do you think Charlie would agree to be a bridesmaid if it meant she had to wear a dress?!

♥ Imagine the fabulous cakes Charlie might make in the future!

♥ Will life get easier for Lottie? Perhaps she'll find a job with a nicer family — or maybe she'll marry a lovely man and start a family of her own!

♥ Do you think Charlie and Robin would still get along if they had to live together?

♥ Will Charlie build a strong relationship with Mark over time?

BEAKER'S

Bonkers Word Blanks

Write a super–silly story with Tracy!

How to play:

⭐ Fill in the blanks with your own words to finish Tracy's letter to Cam. Tracy has given you a hint for each missing word: on each blank, you must use an adjective, noun, verb, place, or part of the body.

⭐ You can use any words you like — the letter doesn't have to make perfect sense when you read it back... in fact, the sillier, the funnier!

Just call me 'teacher'!

Need a helping hand? Tracy's simple grammar guide will keep you right...

ADJECTIVES

These are describing words, such as:

Beautiful

Scary

Disgusting

Incredible

Surprising

Preposterous

Awesome

Bizarre

Brave

NOUNS

A noun is a person, place or thing.

Tracy Beaker

Mum

Doctor

Backpack

Sweets

Telephone

Paris

Home

School

Looking for more inspiration? Dig out your dictionary or thumb through a thesaurus!

VERBS

These are doing words. Here are some examples to get you started:

Cycle

Run

Fly

Cry

Baby Tracy

Laugh

Dance

Scream

Bounce

Swim

Dear Sister Writer,

You will never ever, EVER believe what happened to the _____ Tracy Beaker
ADJECTIVE
at breakfast today! I'd just sat down to a bowl of _____ when
NOUN
Justine-Unbelievably-Clumsy-Littlewood accidentally-on-purpose spilt a WHOLE bottle
of _____ on my _____! My _____ was completely and utterly
NOUN   BODY PART   NOUN
soaked through so I _____ off upstairs to change. (Only after I threw a wet
VERB
_____ at Justine, of course!)
NOUN
I _____ open my wardrobe door and spotted a letter tucked inside my
VERB
_____ pocket. It said 'Tracy' on the envelope and there was a drawing of a
NOUN
_____. I was so _____, I tore it open and out spilled a letter from
NOUN   ADJECTIVE
Peter. You can imagine my disappointment. I mean, Peter is just so _____! But
ADJECTIVE
you'll never guess what the letter said: Peter wants ME to come on his birthday treat
trip to _____.
PLACE
I practically _____ back downstairs to find Peter. He was sitting in the
VERB
_____. His face went _____ when I gave him a big hug. I don't think
PLACE   ADJECTIVE
I've ever seen him so flustered, ha ha. Then it was my turn to go red —
except I was boiling with _____ anger. He's only gone and
ADJECTIVE
invited Justine-Party-Pooper-Littlewood, too!

So, what should I do, Cam? I could always lock Justine in the
_____, or use my Outstanding Powers of Persuasion to convince Peter
PLACE
he should invite _____ instead. If only Justine
NOUN
would _____ to the moon and never come back!
VERB
Write back ASAP.

Peter

Tracy X

How To Mind Map!

A mind map's a great way to plan a story!

Mind mapping is a way of planning a story based on a single word or idea, and it's helpful for breaking a big subject into smaller chunks. Each branch represents a fact or idea and you can make your map as big or small as you like.

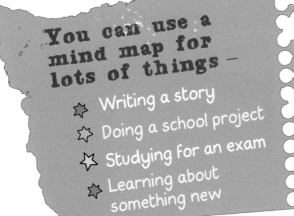

You can use a mind map for lots of things —

- ☆ Writing a story
- ☆ Doing a school project
- ☆ Studying for an exam
- ☆ Learning about something new

DID YOU KNOW?

Mind maps were first created in the 3rd century!

How to make a mind map!

1. Start in the centre by writing or drawing your topic. Make it bright and colourful!

2. Think of things that relate to your topic and write them around your starting point. Make sure everything's connected with a line!

3. Use lots of colours to make it exciting to look at, and to group ideas together.

4. Keep your mind map clear by writing neatly — it helps to write in capital letters.

5. Use pictures — either print them from the internet or draw your own.

If you made a mind map about Tracy Beaker, it might look like this!

Black curly hair

Black eyes

LOOKS

Red jumper

Daring

PERSONALITY

Funny

Fiesty

Justine

Playing with make-up

Eating stew

LIKES

DISLIKES

Elaine

poster paints

sweeties

yum!

Mind Map Quiz!

What story should you plan?

1. You're adventurous
A) Yes   B) No

2. You cry at movies
A) No   B) Yes

3. You love the colour pink
A) No   B) Yes

4. You're good at sports
A) Yes   B) No

5. You can be quite loud
A) Yes   B) No

Mostly A...

A daring action adventure perfectly matches your confident personality!

Mostly B...

You're super-sweet — a dreamy romantic tale is totally you!

Turn over to get started!

My Mind Map

Make your own mind map here!

Tip!
You can use a mind map for anything! You could plan your whole story, plan each character or map out every chapter!

Tip!
Use brightly coloured pens to make each section stand out!

Write your topic here:

Tip!
Why not use pictures instead of words? You can use them as illustrations in your book!

Jacky talks about...
Magazines

When I was 17 DC Thomson started up a new magazine called *Jackie* and I contributed various articles and short stories. The first thing I ever wrote for *Jackie* was a feature about going to your first posh dance — when all your girlfriends get asked up to dance and you don't!

Me at work in the *Jackie* office.

I worked on magazines as a journalist for a couple of years and, after I was married and had my daughter Emma, I wrote hundreds of short stories and serials to help pay the bills. The funniest thing I ever wrote for a magazine was probably an article about Emma when she was young — she was a very naughty baby.

I loved *Girl* comic when I was young, and then I was very fond of teenage magazines called *Petticoat* and *Honey*. Nowadays I might flick through the glossy fashion magazines — but my favourite magazine has to be *The Official Jacqueline Wilson Mag!*

You can make your own magazine with me! Turn the page now!

POW!

JACKY AT

January 18, 1964. Every Thursday   6d

Jackie

for go-ahead teens

Jacky's first writing job was on one of the best-known magazines of all time!

HOW IT ALL BEGAN...

When Jacky was 17 years old, she spotted an advert looking for people to write articles for a brand new magazine. Jacky picked up her pen and wrote an amusing piece all about what it's like to go to a posh dance and be one of the girls who doesn't get asked to dance by a boy.

The editors of the magazine loved the article and offered Jacky a job in Dundee, hundreds of miles away from her home in Kingston-upon-Thames. It was a dream come true for Jacky — she was being offered the chance to write for a living! — so she travelled all the way up to Dundee, ready to report for duty!

However, when she arrived at the hostel where she was supposed to be staying, Jacky found that there had been a mix-up and her room wasn't available. She had to sleep in a linen cupboard for three months!

Jacky's job was to write lots of features that would appeal to the girls who read the magazine — there were photo stories (like comic strips), fashion features, problem pages and lots of interviews with celebrities!

DID YOU KNOW?
The first issue of Jackie came out on January 11, 1964.

Could you be a magazine journalist?

If you answer Yes to more than half of these, journalism could be the job for you!

☐ I love writing!
☐ I always hand in my homework on time.
☐ I'm really creative and always have lots of fab ideas!
☐ I like chatting to people and getting to know them!
☐ I'm always asking questions!
☐ I read lots of magazines!
☐ I'm quite nosy... or inquisitive, as you prefer to say!

MOSTLY YES!
Chatty, inquisitive and great at writing, you'd make a great journalist!

MOSTLY NO!
Hmmm, maybe journalism isn't your thing, but you could still be a great part of a magazine team — turn to page 22 to find the job for you!

Jackie vs **The Official Jacqueline Wilson Mag**

Jackie		Jacqueline Wilson Mag
For go-ahead teens	**Tagline**	Read, write, create
Celebrities	**Cover Star**	JW characters
Twin heart ring	**Gifts**	Stationery, sweets, stickers, tattoos, badges...
"Dreamy picture love stories!"	**Activities**	How to write your own stories
Popstars of the era like The Beatles, Cliff Richard and The Rolling Stones	**Celebrities**	It's all about Jacky and Nick (oh, and Jacob and Lily!)

MARTY'S SUPER MAG MAKER

I'll help you create your very own magazine!

First things first... every magazine needs a fantastic, eye-catching cover. You want your mag to really stand out, so think about using lots of bright colours and interesting pictures & drawings.

Let's look at a JW Mag cover for inspiration...

Fab gifts!
What kind of gifts would you offer?

Design a logo for your magazine.
Make sure you can read it clearly!

Choose a cover star.
It can be a person, object, drawing or photo to tie in with the theme of your mag.

Think up **amazing prizes and competitions** for your readers.

Keep the wording on the cover short and sweet.
You don't want to overload the cover with text.

Speech bubbles and tick-lists
are a great way to let your reader know what's inside.

DAZZLING GIFTS!
☑ AMAZING NOTEBOOK!
☑ SPECTACULAR PENCILS!
☑ MAGNIFICENT BOOK MARK & STICKY NOTE SET!

WIN! ☑ iPad Mini
Everyone wants one!

The Official Jacqueline Wilson Mag

£3.60 #61

WIN! The Diamond doll
Could I be yours?
ONLY in JW Mag!

ISSUE No. 61

DRAW!
Sketch Diamond with me!

LOL!
Super-funny cringes inside!

How to be a brilliant best friend!

STAR BOOK DIAMOND
It's Jacky's NEW story!

MAKE! Rose cupcakes
Pretty!

DO!
☑ PUZZLES
☑ QUIZZES
☑ GAMES
All the fun of the fair!

READ ✦ WRITE ✦ CREATE

Cover gifts and confectionery items may vary and may not be available in all countries. Competitions open to UK residents only, unless otherwise stated.

WHAT'S INSIDE?

It's time to think about the features and activities you want to have inside your mag. Choose from these ideas to build up your content:

- ☐ Puzzles
- ☐ Fabulous fashion
- ☐ Embarrassing cringes
- ☐ Jokes
- ☐ True stories
- ☐ Problems

- ☐ Quizzes & games
- ☐ Recipes
- ☐ Craft projects
- ☐ Interviews with celebrities
- ☐ Letters page
- ☐ Competitions with fab prizes

WRITE IT

Will you write the entire magazine all by yourself, or will you ask your friends to help you? As Editor of your magazine, YOU get to decide who will write what! Jot down everyone's names and their designated pages below:

NAME	PAGES TO WRITE
-----------	--------------------
-----------	--------------------
-----------	--------------------
-----------	-------------
-----------	--------------------

Drawing Mighty Mart is my favourite part!

felt tips

DRAW IT

Bring your pages to life with colourful illustrations and artwork. Use bright colours and frames to make your pictures and drawings really pop! If you're not a very good artist, don't worry — here are a few helpful hints:

- ● Cut out illustrations from old magazines.
- ● Print out pictures from the internet.
- ● Use Nick's How to Draw tips to perfect your drawing skills!
- ● Stick in family photos — be sure to ask permission first!

Turn over the page for quiz templates and tips!

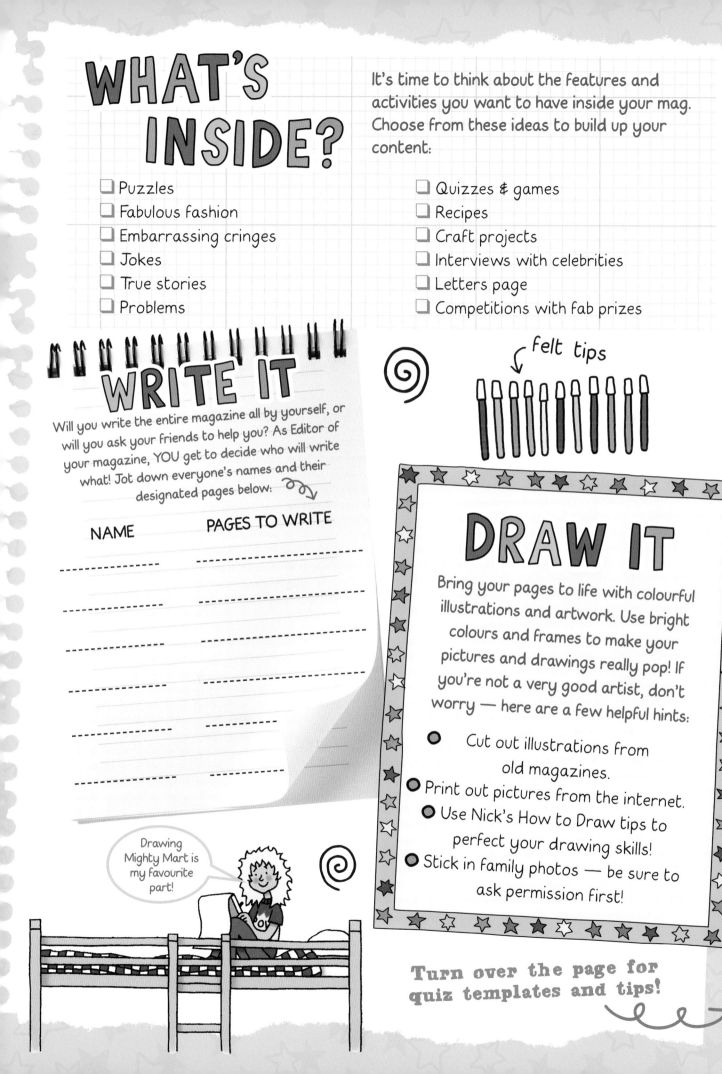

QUIZ-TASTIC TIPS!

Making a flowchart is so much fun! Follow Marty's step-by-step guide to make your very own...

Step 1

Think of a theme or question to base your quiz on. Here are some ideas:

- What's Your Fashion Style?
- Find Your Perfect Pet!
- Which JW Character Are You?
- Discover Your Story Style!
- Are You A Fab Friend?
- Reveal Your Top Talent!

Step 2

Decide on three quite different conclusions and write them in the boxes at the bottom of the chart. These are your outcomes.

Here's an example based on a flowchart for the theme Find Your Perfect Pet:

I like to add drawings to my outcomes!

DOG
You make a fab friend! You love to make people laugh and smile. Your BF knows she can always count on you.

SNAKE
You love to stand out from the crowd and do things differently! You're very creative, outspoken and a little bit quirky!

CAT
You're very independent, especially when it comes to style. You like to mix and match the latest fashions, your way.

Step 3

Fill the circles with simple questions or choices. These are your options. For a pet quiz, you could write options like these...

- You love cuddles
- Creepy-crawlies give you the shivers!
- You like to go for long walks
- You're allergic to fur

Step 4

Label each arrow to finish your flowchart. A simple 'yes' or 'no' format is best. Make sure they're labelled correctly before you test your flowchart on your besties — try it out yourself first!

Now it's your turn!

QUIZ-TASTIC TEMPLATE!

ZAP!

Scan or photocopy this handy template to create your own fun quizzes — POW!

Write your title here!

....

START

A

B

C

What's Your Dream Magazine Job?

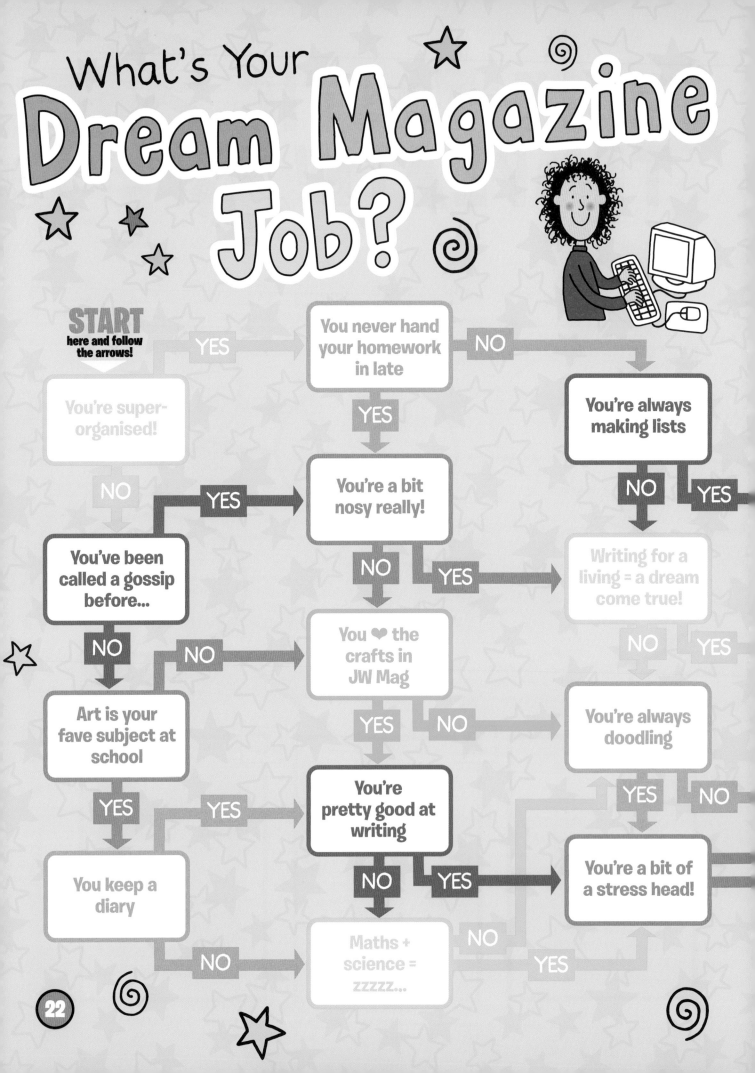

START here and follow the arrows!

You're super-organised!

YES → You never hand your homework in late

NO → You're always making lists

YES (from never hand homework in late) → You're a bit nosy really!

NO → You've been called a gossip before...

YES (from super-organised NO) → You're a bit nosy really!

YES (from making lists) → / **NO** → Writing for a living = a dream come true!

NO (from nosy) → You ❤ the crafts in JW Mag

YES (from nosy) → Writing for a living = a dream come true!

NO (from gossip) → Art is your fave subject at school

NO (from gossip) → You ❤ the crafts in JW Mag

NO (from writing for a living) → / **YES** → You're always doodling

YES (from crafts) → You're pretty good at writing

NO (from crafts) → You're always doodling

YES (from art) → You keep a diary

YES (from art) → You're pretty good at writing

YES (from doodling) → / **NO** → You're a bit of a stress head!

NO (from writing) → / **YES** → You're a bit of a stress head!

NO (from writing) → Maths + science = ZZZZZ...

NO (from diary) → Maths + science = ZZZZZ...

NO / **YES** (from maths + science) → You're a bit of a stress head! / You're always doodling

22

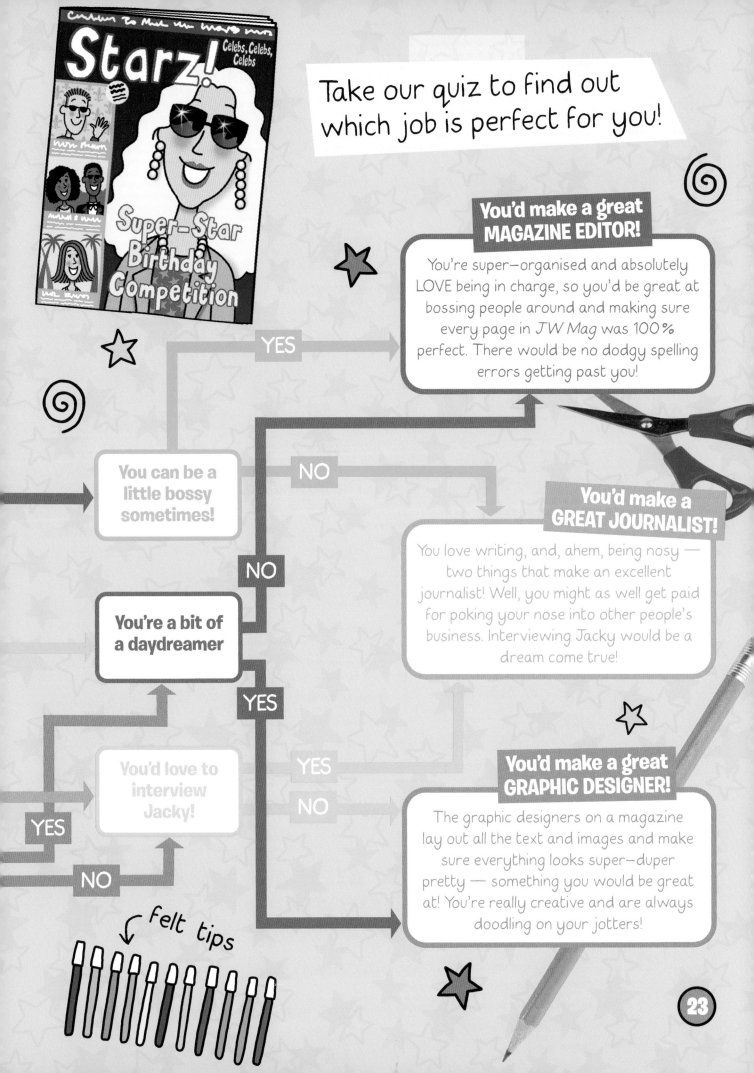

Take our quiz to find out which job is perfect for you!

Starz! Celebs, Celebs, Celebs

Super-Star Birthday Competition

You'd make a great MAGAZINE EDITOR!

You're super-organised and absolutely LOVE being in charge, so you'd be great at bossing people around and making sure every page in *JW Mag* was 100% perfect. There would be no dodgy spelling errors getting past you!

YES

You can be a little bossy sometimes!

NO

You'd make a GREAT JOURNALIST!

You love writing, and, ahem, being nosy — two things that make an excellent journalist! Well, you might as well get paid for poking your nose into other people's business. Interviewing Jacky would be a dream come true!

NO

You're a bit of a daydreamer

YES

YES

You'd love to interview Jacky!

YES

NO

NO

You'd make a great GRAPHIC DESIGNER!

The graphic designers on a magazine lay out all the text and images and make sure everything looks super-duper pretty — something you would be great at! You're really creative and are always doodling on your jotters!

felt tips

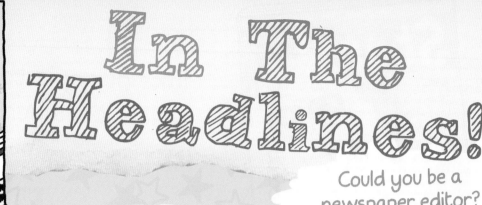

What is a headline?

A headline is the title of a story in a newspaper. It needs to be punchy and attention—grabbing so that people will pick up the newspaper and want to read the story! Journalists spend ages thinking of a good headline.

What's wrong with these headlines?

1 THE DARE GMAE!

2 THOUSANDS EVACUATED FROM FOOTBALL MATCH DUE TO FIRE ALARM INCIDENT HALF WAY THROUGH THE MATCH!

3 WOMAN AND CAT IN BITING INCIDENT!

Answers:
1. There's a spelling mistake in it! Oops!
2. It's too long. People will have lost interest in it.
3. Too vague — you don't know who has bitten who!

Match the headline to the story!

1 The Illustrated Mum!

2 Shiver Me Timbers!

3 Otter Chaos!

A mum has made the news after she got her fiftieth tattoo — more than anyone else in the local area! Her favourite one is of a dolphin.

An old pirate ship has been discovered in the Antarctic. The boat has been buried in an iceberg that had melted, and is dated to the 1800s.

Twenty otters escaped from a local zoo and caused chaos in the local city — whole streets were closed off. Apparently, their cage was left unlocked.

Can you think of some headlines for these stories?

1 A deer wandered into the middle of a motorway yesterday and caused a massive pile up! Luckily, no—one was hurt in the incident

2 A girl called Tracy Beaker has made the news after winning a McDonald's burger—eating competition. She managed 20!

3 A girl has been banned from school because she dyed her hair bright pink. The headteacher tutted, 'It looks like candyfloss!'

Jacky talks about... Memories

I wonder if you've got a memory box — a special box in which you keep photographs, postcards, tiny souvenirs, scraps of favourite outfits, sparkly rings out of Christmas crackers, little scribbled notes passed secretly in class, your very first Valentine? I can't bear to throw anything away so my entire house is like a memory box. I've got all of Emma's drawings and stories from when she went to nursery school, I've got my own diaries and notebooks and manuscripts, I've got thousands of photographs, I've even got some of my childhood toys.

My very first memory was sitting in my pram, being jerked down the step into our back garden. Little children didn't have buggies when I was small, they were pushed around in great big prams. I was probably about two.

My most wonderful memory is the day Emma was born. The day a publisher said they wanted to publish my first book comes pretty close!

This is a house I shared with friends

My favourite doll

Emma and me

Write about your first memory here:

25

Photo Fabulous!

Match your photos to Jacky's!

A picture of you as a baby!

Jacky was born on December 17, 1945, in Bath!

Jacky's mum is called Biddy, her dad was called Harry!

A picture of you with your parents!

Jacky was given the nickname Jacky Daydream at school!

This necklace is Jacky's favourite piece of jewellery!

Jacky's best friend from school, Chris, is still one of her friends now!

A picture of you with your BF!

Jacky's star sign is Sagittarius!

A picture of you on your birthday!

This is Jacky with her daughter, Emma!

A picture of you with a special family member!

When I Was Was 10...

I lived in Ravenshead, a village in Nottinghamshire with my mum, dad, brother, two sisters, a cat called Henry and a tortoise called Joey.

I wanted to be an artist.

My most treasured possession then was my first watch.

A TV show I never missed was *Vision On*, a programme with lots of art in it.

I wanted to look like Mick Robertson, who was a presenter on a groovy children's TV programme called *Magpie*. He wore very trendy clothes and had amazing curly hair.

My film I liked was *The Railway Children*. **A film I disliked was** cartoon *The Aristocats* – I thought it was really boring.

What I really looked like was a freckly 10 year–old with a wonky fringe.

I really liked going to the monthly kids' disco at the village hall.

© George Wilkes

28

Brilliant Brainteasers!

Test your memory with these fun puzzles and quizzes!

Picture Perfect

Look at the picture grid for one minute, then cover it up and draw everything you can remember into the blank grid.

How many did you get right?

0-4 Memory Blank!
You didn't score brilliantly — why not try it again to give your memory a boost?

5-8 Moderate Memory!
You slipped up on a couple but can remember most of the grid — well done!

9-11 Magic Memory!
You have a tremendous memory — you could remember absolutely anything!

Wonderful Words!

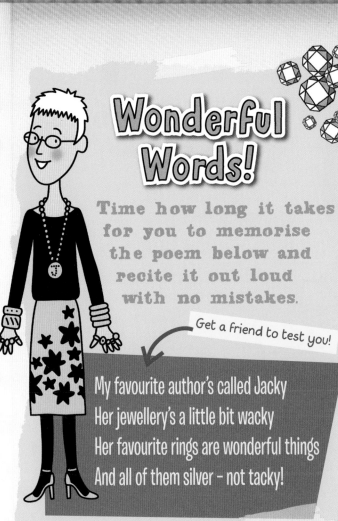

Time how long it takes for you to memorise the poem below and recite it out loud with no mistakes.

Get a friend to test you!

My favourite author's called Jacky
Her jewellery's a little bit wacky
Her favourite rings are wonderful things
And all of them silver - not tacky!

1-5 minutes

You're super—fast and super—smart — you could easily become an actress and memorise your lines. Top marks!

6-12 minutes

You've got a good memory but got a little bit stuck — try memorising the poem again and see if you can do it faster.

13 minutes or more

Memorising lines isn't your thing, but that's okay because we bet you could write a great poem instead!

Your Memory Personality!

Discover how you remember things best!

Start

You love writing lists

YES → You find it easy to concentrate

NO → You fidget a lot

NO → You like to be busy

YES → You like to be busy

NO / YES

You fidget a lot

YES / YES → You like trying new things

You like to be busy — NO → You have lots of stationery

You like trying new things — YES

NO

NO / YES

Do & Learn!

You like to keep busy, so science experiments and trying new recipes are your strong point!
Try: Taking pictures to jog your memory!

Study Hard!

You remember things by reading, writing and studying hard. You excel in subjects like English and History.
Try: A revision timetable!

Make a Memory Box!

Decorate an old box and use it to store your most precious mementoes!

Make this box!

You'll need:

- A box with a lid
- Patterned tape
- Scissors
- Fabric
- Glue
- Letter beads
- Stick-on gems

① Start by covering your box with the patterned tape. If you don't have patterned tape, you can make your own! Just stick patterned paper to strips of double-sided sticky tape, then peel off the backing when you're ready to use it!

② Next, line your box using fabric. Use the different sides of the box as a guide to help you cut them to size. Stick down the panels with glue.

Why not?

Decorate it another way!

- Stick photos to the outside of the box – ask permission first if you're using originals, otherwise, you can print them from the computer!

- Wrap the box in pretty wrapping paper, then cover with clear sticky plastic!

- Create a cool collage of all your favourite JW characters by cutting them out of old magazines!

- Paint your version of the cover of your favourite JW book!

Your box should look like this

③ Now, embellish your box! Add letter beads to spell out 'My memories' on the lid, and stick on some sparkly gems! If you don't have letter beads, you could cut out letters from card or old magazines! Now fill with precious trinkets!

What will you store in your memory box?

- **Photos**
- **Jewellery**
- **Letters**
- **Ticket stubs**
- **Cake toppers from birthday cakes**
- **Holiday souvenirs**
- **Pressed flowers**

JW Memory Test!

Bonus points if you can name the book too!

Guess which characters these memories belong to!

1 We ended up in a refuge where all the little kids kept crying and one of the women tried to nick all our Danny stuff. Mum didn't half clobber her when she caught her — no one messes with Mum's Danny Kilman collection.

Name *Little darlings*

Book ....

2 When we were down one end of the street and got our first glimpse of the Royal, I thought it looked very grand indeed. But the Royal started to look a bit shabby the nearer we got...

Name *bed and Breakfast star*

Book ....

3 There was a letter inside and some sort of brochure. I peered at it as best I could. I saw the words boarding school. My heart started beating fast.

Name ....

Book ....

4 I flipped through the book furiously — and then stopped. There was a photo of this girl about my age. She even looked a bit like me, skinny and pale.

Name ....

Book ....

5 Will acts like he doesn't know me at school. A lot of the time he acts like we're strangers at home too. It's ever since he found out. It's changed everything.

Name ....

Book ....

Jacky talks about...
Friends & Family

If you were asked to describe my books I expect you'd call them family stories — but they're frequently unhappy families! I had a reasonably ordinary childhood, but my mum and dad quarreled a lot and eventually split up, and I suppose that did have some kind of effect on me. I was determined to make my own marriage work — but that didn't happen either. However, I knew from the day that Emma was born that I totally adored her, and I'm so happy to say that now she's grown up we're still tremendously close.

Sometimes I think you can be as close to your friends as you are your family. My best friend when I was young was a girl called Chris — we're still close all these many years later. My best friend now is Trish, who takes many of the photos of me used in the annual and magazines.

Me on the day I was made a Dame with Emma and my best friend, Trish.

With my childhood best friend, Chris.

Turn over for lots of friendship fun!
o Make a prezzie for your BF!
o Take the best friend quiz!
o Create a quirky family!
And lots more!

What's Your FRIENDSHIP FAIL?

What stops you from being the best friend in the whole world?

① Your best friend texts you. You text back...

a) Straight away. Duh, she's your best friend!

b) When you get off the phone from your other mate!

c) About three hours later. You completely forgot — oops!

d) During the ad break of the TV show you're watching.

② When was the last time you spilled a secret?

a) Not too long ago. You totally forgot it was a secret!

b) You wouldn't. And if anyone has blabbed yours, watch out!

c) Oops... you do this all the time! You love a good gossip.

d) You never, ever have. You're totally trustworthy!

③ You last hung out in a big group of friends...

a) Yesterday. You love swapping secrets with all your mates!

b) Recently. You arranged the whole thing, naturally.

c) Ages ago. You prefer it when it's just the two of you.

d) A couple of weeks ago. Your bff organised it all!

④ Your gran buys you a big box of sweets. You...

a) Throw a strop if anyone tries to pinch any!

b) Split them with your bestie — even your fave ones!

c) Take them to school to share with everyone.

d) Eat them all yourself. Mmmm... you love sweeties!

⑤ In your friendship group, you are...

a) The super-chatty one.

b) The chilled out one.

c) The quiet one. You're a bit shy really!

d) The stroppy one. You can be a bit of a diva!

⑥ If you found your friend's diary, you would...

a) Ignore it and carry on with what you were doing.

b) Read it, and be horrified if you found your name mentioned!

c) Read it — then accidentally talk about what you'd read afterwards!

d) Not care really. Diaries are far too much drama!

⑦ The last time you and your mates had a sleepover you...

a) Zoned out of all the girl chat and fell asleep instead.

b) Fell out over the movie choice. What's new?

c) Told your bestie the biggest secret ever!

d) Got told off for talking all night by your friend's dad!

Now add up your score!

If you got 7 – 12
You want your bestie all to yourself...

You're super-loyal and really love having a best friend, but you prefer it when it's just the two of you. You don't want to share your bff with anyone! Why not hang out with different people from time to time? Then you'll find that when you do see each other, you have even more to gossip about!

If you got 13 – 18
You're too much of a chatterbox!

No one ever gets any sleep at a sleepover when you're there! It's great that you're so fun and bubbly, but it's not so good when you accidentally blurt out your bff's secrets! Try being a little bit more trustworthy and thinking before you speak, and you'll still get told all the juiciest bits of gossip!

If you got 19 – 23
You're a bit too laid-back...

You have a great group of friends, but sometimes you forget just how great they are. You don't reply to texts, drift off during girly chats, and sometimes even forget about plans you've made. It's fab to be so laid-back, but maybe you should remind them that they all mean a lot to you!

If you got 24 – 28
You want your own way all the time!

You are a bit of a diva sometimes, aren't you? You're happiest when everything is going exactly your way — and you've even been known to throw a Tracy Beaker-sized strop if it isn't. Chill out a bit and let your other mates choose the sleepover movies for once... you might enjoy it!

The Perfect Prezzie!

Sew this pretty gift for your BF!

You'll need:
Felt
Patterned fabric
Scissors
Needle
Thread
Scrap material
Beads, buttons or other embellishments

Old tights are perfect!

1 Cut out two shapes from felt, then some smaller versions in contrasting fabric or felt.

2 Stitch the layers of felt and fabric to one of your larger shapes — you can use any stitch you like!

3 Now stitch the two large shapes together, leaving an opening. A running stitch or blanket stitch works best for this step!

Stuff some scraps of material into the opening, then sew it shut.

4 Add any embellishments to the front of your shape, then work out what kind of gift you're going to turn it in to...

Why not?

Try some other shapes or patterns, like hearts and flowers!

Make a marvellous magnet!

Just glue a magnet strip to the back!

Make it into a brooch!

Just add a brooch pin to the back!

Create a scented sachet!

Just add a few drops of essential oils to the fabric stuffing, or use dried lavender!

Create a cool hanging ornament!

Just add a ribbon between the two large shapes before you stitch it up!

Trace round these shapes to make some pretty hearts and roses!

39

How To Cope When...

Having BF bother? Your favourite JW characters are here to help!

She Has A Secret

Your BF has just spilled the biggest secret ever...

Treasure says... My best friend India told me a huge secret and it was really hard to watch her go through a difficult time. If your friend tells you a secret, then that's exactly what it is — a secret. You'd be devastated if she blabbed things you've told her to everyone. However, if the secret is something serious and someone could get hurt, you need to speak to an adult and get her the help she needs.

She Moves Away

You've been friends for years and years... Then one day your BF moves hundreds of miles away!

Gemma says... Alice and I have been BFs since we were babies and then she moved all the way to Scotland! I found it really hard and I didn't like her new friend Flora one tiny bit. I regret being so mean to her, though — I had to let Alice make her own friends in her new town. Remember that things are just as difficult for your friend as they are for you and it's not easy making a whole new group of friends. What matters is staying friends, no matter how near or far you live!

Remember to have fun with your BF and cheer her up!

You Lose Her

Losing a friend to illness or an accident is devastating and life-changing...

Jade says... I was so upset when my BF Vicky died — I didn't think I'd ever get over it. I wish I'd spoken to someone about how I felt, like a parent or teacher. Now I understand it's natural to feel angry, upset and alone. By getting help, you can talk through your problems and realise that it's not your fault — no one could have stopped what happened. You'll always remember your friend, but those horrible feelings will fade in time.

If things are getting too much, ask your friend to talk to an adult and get the help she needs.

You Fall Out

You and your BF haven't been seeing eye to eye and you've just had a massive argument!

Ellie says... Arguments often happen in friendships — you spend so much time with each other, it's natural that you'll disagree from time to time. What's important is how you mend your friendship. Try to see things from your friend's point of view — you might have said or done some nasty things too! Open up to your BF and tell her you're sorry, then put it all in the past and get your friendship back on track!

Try to see things from your BF's point of view.

Family Life Is Tough

Arguments, parents splitting up and nightmare siblings — sometimes life at home can be stressful.

Lily says... I wish I'd told someone what was going on at home. Sometimes things don't go as planned and there can be arguments or separations, but it's important to remember that you love your family and they love you too. Be grown up about it and ask to speak to your parents, then calmly explain how you feel. They'll realise how mature you're being and will want to help you.

Create a quirky family for your story!

Roll & Write Story-teller

Families come in all shapes and sizes — just like mine!

How To Play

⭐ Pick family members from the list below. You can have as few or as many as you like.

⭐ Roll the dice to choose a setting or scenario. There are 20 different outcomes to choose from!

⭐ Now write a story based on your unique family. Have fun!

Family Members

IRRITATING STEP-SISTER	FRAIL GRANDFATHER	STRICT MOTHER
IDENTICAL TWIN BOYS	GENTLE FOSTER MOTHER	PROTECTIVE BROTHER
KINDLY AUNT	MISCHIEVOUS TODDLER	JEALOUS COUSIN

Jacky talks about... Pets & Animals

With Jacob when he was a kitten!

When I was a child I always longed for a pet, but we lived in a small flat, and we weren't allowed to have cats or dogs. I decided I would have many pets when I grew up — but for a long time I travelled around too much to make this possible. It's so lovely now that I have my two beautiful grey and white rescue cats, Jacob and Lily. I did also have my slinky black stray cat Thomas who lived with me for two years — but sadly he wandered off one day and never came back. I do hope he's safe and living happily with someone else now.

Jacob and Lily give me so much joy. Jacob is especially cuddly early in the morning and loves to be brushed then. Lily is more of a night–time girl — she often curls up beside my pillow and gently sucks my finger–tips.

Enjoying cuddles with Lily.

My favourite wild animal is definitely a lemur — I think they're such beautiful little creatures and I love the way they lie on their backs sunbathing when it's hot. They're also so sweet when they go to sleep in a huddle, with their tails all coiled round neatly.

I'm stupidly scared of many types of fish, especially sharks. I'm trying hard to overcome my fear because I know they're amazing and interesting.

Relaxing on my bed!

Do You Know?

Which of Jacky's characters is also scared of sharks?

45

Answer: Lola Rose

Battersea
Paws & Purrs

Shadow

Star

Battersea Dogs & Cats Home has cared for more than three million animals since it was founded 150 years ago. Let's meet some of the four-legged lovelies who found happy new homes, thanks to Battersea!

Shadow & Star

Best friends, Shadow and Star, dreamed of finding the perfect home together. Their wish was fulfilled when they were adopted by Tibetan monk, Geshe Tashi Tsering.

The pair now live in perfect peace and harmony at the Jamyang Buddhist Centre in London, snoozing the day away in the sunny courtyard and mingling with the many visitors to the centre. They've even been given new names to match their spiritual surroundings — Star has been renamed as 'Tara' (the Tibetan word for 'star') and Shadow is now called 'Kala'. Sweet!

WOW!

Battersea rehomes over 2000 cats every year! That's a LOT of cat food needed... 33,488 pouches, in fact!

What's In A Name?

The most popular names given to rehomed Battersea cats are Charlie and Oscar for boys, and Coco and Bella for girls!

Ray

Poor little Ray was abandoned outside a veterinary clinic, completely blind and all alone. The staff at Battersea lovingly cared for Ray over the next month and gave him the confidence he needed to live without eyesight.

Ray's photo was put up on the Battersea website and he was an instant hit! Lots and lots of people wanted to give him a new home, but there was only one lady for Ray — Miss Longbottom.

Thanks to Battersea, Ray quickly settled into his new home and gets around with ease. Ray loves his lady owner to bits — and she loves him just as much in return!

Stories

Waggy Dog Tail!

Jessie is a seven-month-old Staffordshire Bull Terrier. Sadly, some people think these dogs look dangerous, which couldn't be further from the truth — Staffies are actually very loving and loyal, and most make a great family pet. Thankfully, the staff at Battersea Dogs & Cats Home know just how amazing these little dogs really are. They took Jessie in and looked after her until she was rehomed by a lovely family...

Did You Know?

Staffies are often called the 'Nanny Dog' because they're generally very good with children.

Jessie's new owners say:

"We're so glad we saw Jessie on the website. We all adored her picture, and fell in love with her the first time we met her — she was full of beans and very inquisitive!"

Jessie is very happy in her new home. She has made great friends with the family's grandchildren and likes to follow them everywhere!

JW & Battersea

Battersea has a special place in my heart.

Jacky is a great supporter of Battersea and is very proud to be an Ambassador for the charity. Recently, she was very excited to be invited along to the charity's annual fundraising party, the amazing Collars & Coats Gala Ball!

We raised lots of money for the charity!

Jacky has even adopted two cats of her very own — Jacob and Lily...

I was a little stray kitten without a bed to call my own. Not any more! I have all the home comforts a cat could ever want.

I'm so grateful to Battersea — they nursed me to health when I was a poorly kitten and found me the perfect home with Jacky and Jacob.

Want to find out more about Battersea Dogs & Cats Home and the adorable animals in their care? Log on to www.battersea.org.uk

We Love Lemurs!

Find out more about Jacky's favourite wild animals!

The females are the leaders of the lemur families.

Lemurs are very sociable. They like to hang out together in big groups called troops.

Lemur means spirit of the night!

Mums carry their babies in their mouths till they're old enough to cling on.

Millions of years ago, lemurs were the size of gorillas!

Lemurs are primates, like monkeys. However, they don't use their tails to hang from trees like other primates — instead, they use their hands and feet to grip as they move through the branches.

The pygmy mouse lemur is the smallest primate in the world — only a teeny-tiny six centimetres long!

Indri lemurs don't have tails!

There are almost 100 different types of lemur.

Lemurs are only found living wild in Madagascar — a small island off the east coast of Africa — and the Comoro Islands.

They don't see very well in colour but they have an amazing sense of smell!

How To Draw Lemurs!

Nick shows you in three easy steps!

Why not add some texture to the lemur by using cotton wool for the fur — just use very thin paint to add colour to this!

1. Start by drawing the head — it's very much like the shape of a cat's head, but the ears are slightly bigger! Next add some of the body and the tail!

2. Add in the lemur's legs and paws — the paws at the front are very similar to human hands! Now sketch in the lemur's facial features.

3. Finally, add the lemur's other legs and paws and colour him in! Use a black pencil for the detail — press it firmly for the colour on the tail and face, and use it lightly over the body.

RANDOM ANIMALS!

Create your very own crazy creature!

What to do:
Roll a dice for each body part, then draw them all together in the space on the next page! You can roll again and again to come up with lots of strange combos!

HEAD

1 Cat
2 Pug
3 Rabbit
4 Lion
5 Eagle
6 Penguin

BODY

1 Deer
2 Lamb
3 Hedgehog
4 Tortoise
5 Snail
6 Cheetah

FEET

1 Duck
2 Poodle
3 Chicken
4 Kangaroo
5 Panther
6 Horse

TAIL

1 Fox
2 Peacock
3 Whale
4 Tiger
5 Mouse
6 Fish

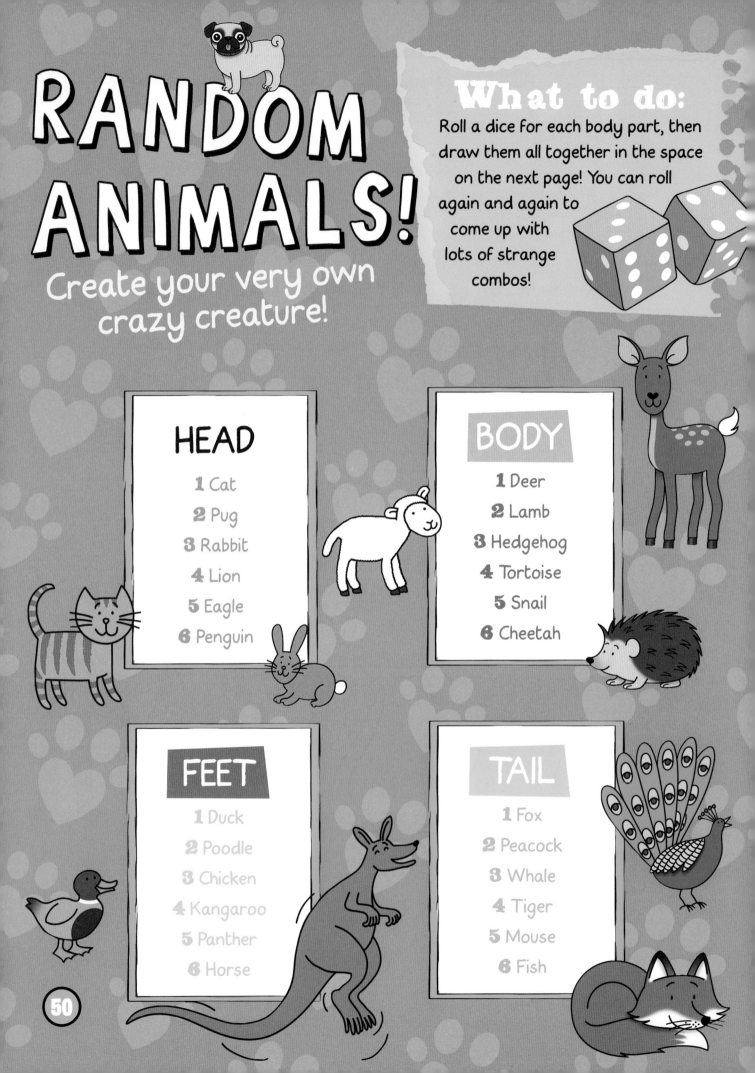

Draw your amazing animal here!

PB and Banana Dog Cookies

Dogs ♥ these!

You'll need:

- 280g wholemeal flour
- 50g rolled oats
- 2 beaten eggs
- 3 ripe mashed bananas
- 125g peanut butter
- 240ml water

1 Heat the oven to 150°C/300°F/gas mark 2. Line two baking trays with greaseproof paper and brush with a little vegetable oil.

2 Mix together the flour and oats in a large bowl.

3 In a separate bowl, stir together the mashed bananas, beaten eggs, peanut butter and water.

4 Make a little well in the flour mixture and pour in the banana mix. Stir thoroughly. The dough will be quite sticky.

5 Drop 50p–sized balls of dough on to the cookie sheets and gently flatten with a fork. Brush the tops with a little milk or beaten egg then bake for 30 – 35 minutes.

Leave to cool on the tray for 5 minutes, then move to a wire rack to continue cooling. The treats will keep for a week in an airtight container.

☆ Not for dogs who need a wheat–free diet.
★ Chocolate is poisonous to dogs and cats – so don't feed them normal cookies!

Tip: Don't give your pet too many treats – one or two a day is enough.

Make kitten crackers and catmint tea!

Lily and Jacob's Afternoon Tea!

catmint

1 Heat the oven to 180°C/350°F/gas mark 4. Line a baking tray with greaseproof paper.

2 In a large bowl, mash the fish with a fork. Now mix in the rest of the ingredients and bring together into a dough.

3 Roll out on a floured board to around 1cm thick and cut into treat-sized shapes.

4 Bake for around 20 minutes until golden. Leave to cool and harden.

You'll need:

- 1 can of pilchards or sardines (undrained)
- 125g flour
- 160g cornmeal or polenta
- 80ml water

Catmint Tea

- Snip off two or three catmint leaves and pour hot water over them.
- Leave to brew like ordinary tea and strain out the leaves.
- Allow to cool and then treat your cat to a special drink with their snacks.

Tip: Make little holes in the centre with a kebab skewer before baking then thread the treats on to some twine to make an instant toy!

Always ask an adult before using any kitchen equipment.

WHICH ANIMAL ARE YOU?

Are you a super-serious owl — or are you always monkeying around?

START
You're a bit of a bookworm.

NO

NO

You love a movie night!

YES

You like bananas. Nom nom nom!

YES

You always get the giggles in class!

NO

You never sit still!

NO

YES

You love learning new things!

NO

You love to sleep in. Zzzzz...

YES

You like playing pranks!

NO

YES

NO

YES

YES

You're an owl...

You're quite studious and love reading — you pay attention in class and there's no chance of you messing around! You're always impressing your friends with all your knowledge — you seem to know everything! Wow.

54

You're a monkey...

There's never a quiet moment when you're around! You're really bubbly and silly — you're always the person who gets the giggles in the middle of maths class! You're also a big fan of bananas — yummy!

You're a koala...

Just like a koala, you're not really one for rushing around! You're laid back and don't mind a lie in on a Saturday morning. You also love a movie night with lots of munchies — you draw the line at eucalyptus leaves, though!

Art & Creativity

I can't remember a time when I wasn't interested in art. When I was in the infants I got terribly excited about making a picture of a man out of some autumn leaves stuck on to paper. I think that's my earliest artistic memory. By the time I was in Year 4 I was taking my drawing pretty seriously and I didn't know whether to be pleased or cross when a teacher held up my attempt at a medieval lady in a pointy hat and said it really wasn't very accurate, but it was great that I'd drawn it with so much enthusiasm. I still tend to give pointy hats to princesses whenever I have to draw them.

Nick aged 6!

At home I drew all the time and my parents made sure I had plenty of paper and art materials to experiment with. I spent most of my pocket money on extra drawing pads and felt tipped pens — especially the black ones. I entered any art competition that I came across in newspapers or on children's television programmes and once or twice I was a prize winner, which really boosted my confidence. As I didn't get the chance to do much art at secondary school I joined an art club and enjoyed it a lot, even though I was the youngest member by about 40 years!

When I left school I did what nearly all the professional artists I know did, and went off to art college. My first year there I got a bit of a shock because I had to draw from real life instead of creating pictures purely out of my imagination, but I soon began to see how important life drawing was in helping me look at things more thoroughly and improving my drawing skills.

I didn't become a children's book illustrator straight away, in fact I spent quite a few years drawing pictures for magazines, packaging and educational books before I was given my first children's book to work on. But now I've illustrated around 250 books and more than 50 of them have been for Jacqueline Wilson. It's a wonderful way to earn a living but it can be hard work too (no one ever believes that, but it's true!). And it's funny to think I still spend nearly every day doing the same activity that gave me the most pleasure all those years ago when I was little more than a toddler!

How Nick Became An Artist...

Nick shares his secrets!

Nick loved drawing from a young age. After enjoying art lessons at school — and drawing lots in his spare time! — he did a year-long foundation art course at Manchester Polytechnic. He really enjoyed studying here as it gave him the opportunity to try lots of different art styles! After this, he studied graphic design at St Martin's School Of Art in London.

When he was younger, Nick loved drawing scenes featuring his local shopping centre, where he could cram lots of different people and details in the scene.

Nick drew this scene from his imagination!

Look at all the detail!

What inspired you to start drawing?
It was just something that I instinctively loved doing from practically the first time I picked up a crayon.

When did you realise you had a talent for art?
I'd always enjoyed drawing but when a picture I'd drawn at home and taken into school was pinned up in the school hall it really helped me believe that I must be good at it, because only the best work went up in the hall!

When you were younger, did you ever get frustrated that something you were drawing wasn't turning out the way you wanted?
I did get frustrated when pictures went wrong and I was such a perfectionist that I'd often waste a lot of paper giving up after having drawn just a few lines. On the other hand, in art lessons at school I got very good at finishing my pictures by the end of the lesson, when other children were only halfway through. Completing your drawings is really important if you want to be an artist, and something that helped me was when I started using little paper patches to cover up mistakes that couldn't be rubbed out.

A view from Nick's student kitchen!

What was your favourite place that you studied at and why?

I thoroughly enjoyed my foundation year at art school in Manchester. That's when you spend three terms having a go at all kinds of art: drawing, painting, sculpture, photography, even performance art. Mostly I did drawing from real life, and I loved it.

Even Nick thinks Tremendous Tracy is the best!

Is there anything you find impossible to draw?

I'm not wild about drawing things from tricky angles, like from a bird's eye or worm's eye view. Certain vehicles like motorbikes are quite tricky to get right, and so, funnily enough, are hamsters and gerbils. Alsatian dogs are extremely hard! But a professional illustrator has to be prepared to draw anything!

Apart from illustrating Jacky's books, what are the best and worst illustration/design jobs that you've done?

I once drew an illustration for the box of a cassette (this was a long time ago — before CDs) on how to speak business German. The designer who hired me was never satisfied and I had to make endless, endless changes. It was very boring. It's hard to choose a best job. I always like to think that the job I'm working on will turn out to be my finest work ever!

Which illustration that you've drawn for one of Jacky's books are you most proud of?

The illustrations of Tracy Beaker. It gives me a huge thrill that her image is instantly recognisable to so many children.

What are your art essentials?

2B and 6B pencils. Layout paper (very thin sheets you can just about see through) for rough drawings. Cartridge paper for final drawings. A light box is a fantastic tool for a professional artist. It's basically a box with a Perspex top and a lightbulb underneath which means you can trace from your rough drawings onto quite thick paper.

If you weren't an artist, what would you like to have a job as instead?

I think I'd like to be a set designer for films or television.

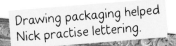

Drawing packaging helped Nick practise lettering.

Turn to page 60 for Nick's drawing tips!

57

How To Draw Nick!

Sketch your favourite illustrator!

1 Pick up a pencil and draw an oval with two ears for Nick's head. Add two diamond shapes for his shirt collar.

2 Sketch the collar of Nick's jumper, and draw his arms and upper body.

3 Copy the picture carefully to draw Nick holding a pencil. Fill in his eyes, eyebrows, neck and mouth. (Doesn't Nick look different without his beard?!)

4 Draw lots of little lines for Nick's beard. Finish his jumper with horizontal lines to create a stripe—tastic design. Now colour him in!

58

Nick's Tip!

Why not design a new jumper for me? I like bright colours and striking patterns!

Draw Nick here!

Nick's Speedy Sketch

Cute babies are one of my favourite things to draw!

1

2

3

NICK'S SKETCHING SECRETS!

Always sketch in pencil first – that way, any mistakes can just be rubbed out! I like to use a 2B or 3B pencil.

Draw lots and lots and lots and always try to finish your pictures!

When sketching hands, just draw five banana shapes! It's so much easier than worrying about all the finger shapes and it's so obvious what they are, you don't need to worry about fingernails!

Practise drawing everyday items from around the house. When I was younger, I liked to draw packaging from the foods in my mum's kitchen cupboards! Items like these are great for practising texture and lettering!

Tracy's Faces!

Facial expressions can give a great sense of the emotion in a picture — just check out these pictures of Tracy! Can you tell how she's feeling?

------------- ------------- -------------

------------- ------------- -------------

Now you try drawing some facial expressions for Tracy!

TIP!
Look in the mirror and make some faces. Now draw what you see!

Start here!

Nick's Sketching Challenge! Can you complete the challenge?

Sketch the cover of your favourite JW book!

Draw a picture of your favourite belonging!

Great work!

Sketch a picture of your favourite animal!

Draw and colour in a flower!

Draw a self-portrait!

Sketch the scene from your bedroom window!

Nearly there!

Well done! Here's a medal!

1ST

felt tips

Draw Your Daydream!

Do you ever daydream about how you would like your life to be? Imagine living in a mansion surrounded with all the things you love and wearing the coolest outfits. Whatever your dream is, now you can draw it!

dream house

Dream Room Ideas!

A secret room only you know about!

Big fluffy cushions and a comfy sofa.

A massive flat-screen TV.

A Jacuzzi to relax in.

Bunk beds for your BFs to sleep over.

A slide to take you down to the front door.

A remote control that means you never have to get up!

Fast car

vroom!

Dream Outfit Ideas!

A fabulous dress covered in sequins, complete with really high heels and a gorgeous hair cut.

Super-cool jeans and a t-shirt with the latest must-have trainers.

An amazing walk-in wardrobe full of the latest trends.

Why not?

○ Draw your ideal holiday destination! Perhaps you'll sketch yourself next to the Eiffel Tower!

○ Draw other dream items — how about a cute-as-can-be puppy or your own art studio like Nick Sharratt's?

○ Draw your dream job — you could be a zookeeper, a high-flying superstar or make amazing scientific discoveries!

Draw your ideal life here!

Who will be in your picture? You could have lots of family and friends or just have the place to yourself!

I'd love to live in a seaside house where I could run out of my front door and be on the beach in a matter of seconds.

You could cut out pictures from magazines and stick them to your drawing for a realistic look!

Are You the Next Nick Sharratt?

What sort of artist should you be?

Tick the statements that sound most like you...

☐ You don't care what other people think.

☐ You're super organised!

☐ Nick Sharratt has the best job ever!

☐ You're good at following instructions!

☐ Art is your fave subject, hands down.

☐ You like to work with other people!

☐ Working on a magazine = awesome!

☐ You heart the JW illustrations!

☐ You're quite bossy!

☐ You're a bit of a daydreamer!

☐ Your homework is always in on time!

☐ You're always doodling on your school jotter!

Now count up all the statements you agreed with, and work out which colour you ticked the most...

Mostly Purple...

You have a huge imagination and are constantly being inspired by everything around you, so you'd make a fantastic artist! You could spend hours in your painting studio letting your creative juices flow. We expect to hear about you winning a prestigious art prize in the future!

Mostly Pink...

One of your favourite things about the Jacqueline Wilson books is Nick's illustrations! You love doodling and are a pro at following instructions, so you'd be great at working with book authors to come up with the perfect character design!

Mostly Blue...

You're creative, but you're also super organised — so you'd be excellent as a graphic designer on a magazine. You'd lay out the pages, design a beautiful cover, and chase up the journalists to make sure everything goes to press on time! Phew!

Jacky talks about... Parties and Sleepovers

I love going to parties, seeing all my friends and having good things to eat and drink, and dancing till late. However, I'm very scared of giving my own parties! I always worry that not enough people will turn up, or that they won't have a good time. I promised all my friends I'd give a big house—warming party. Well, I've lived in my house seven years now, and the party still hasn't happened!

I only had two small parties when I was young, because we lived in a tiny flat and there wasn't really room. I loved going to all my friends' parties though. In those days we played all sorts of games like Squeak Piggy Squeak and Blind Man's Bluff and Statues and best of all, Murder in the Dark. You had a big birthday tea of sandwiches and jelly and ice cream and birthday cake, and had a very modest going—home present — a comb or a biro or a notebook. I know it's often very different nowadays.

The most fun party I've been to was my neighbour's 50th birthday party, where we all had to dress up as James Bond characters.

The swankiest party I've attended was the Queen's 80th birthday party, which had a children's literature theme. There were many famous children's authors attending, and two thousand children and their families. I was Children's Laureate at the time, so it was my job to introduce the Queen to everyone!

Me with JK Rowling at the Queen's party!

Photo by Trish...

Turn over for amazing party ideas...

Amy's Sleepover

Lantern Balls

You'll need:
* Patterned and coloured card
* A ruler * Hole punch
* Paper fasteners * Thread or string

1 Measure and cut out 20 strips of card. Each strip should measure around 20cm long x 3cm wide.

2 Punch a hole in both ends of each strip.

3 Bundle the strips and pop a paper fastener through the holes at the top. Fasten to secure. Do the same for the bottom holes.

4 Gently start to fan out each strip. The lantern will soon begin to take shape, just like this.

5 Tie a length of thread or string round the paper fastener to finish your lantern.

Hang up your lanterns in your bedroom or wherever your sleepover is going to take place. Your besties will love them!

Tip! Use shorter lengths of card to make a smaller lantern, or longer lengths to make it bigger.

Amazing Decorations

Paper Pom-poms

You'll need:
* Sheets of coloured tissue paper (8 sheets for each pom-pom)
* Thread or string

1 Lay out eight sheets of tissue paper, one on top of the other. Fold the layered sheets in a concertina, as if you were making a fan.

2 Tie a length of string in the middle of the fan shape, leaving a long end for you to hang your pom-pom from. It should look like this

3 Gently flatten your fan before rounding off both ends with a pair of scissors to make a petal shape.

4 Begin to gently tease apart each layer of tissue paper. Don't worry too much if you rip it — this only adds to the effect.

5 Carefully fluff up the layers to get a rounded flower shape. Your finished pom-pom is now ready to hang!

Tip! Use lots of different coloured tissue paper to make a rainbow of pom-poms!

Bella's Brilliant Recipes!

My favourite sleepover snacks!

Fun and easy to make!

Bitesize Banana Splits!

You'll need:

- 1 banana
- 75g milk chocolate
- Rainbow sprinkles
- Squirty cream
- Glacé cherries
- Truffle cases

You could swap the banana for pineapple chunks or kiwi fruit!

① Chop banana into 1–inch slices and set aside.

② Break chocolate into chunks and place in a microwave proof bowl. Heat the chocolate in the microwave for 12 seconds then remove and stir. Continue to do this till the chocolate is melted and smooth.

Remember to stir the chocolate regularly or it might burn!

③ Shake a layer of sprinkles into the bottom of the truffle cases then spoon in chocolate till half full. Push a banana into each then add sprinkles on top. Place on a plate and leave in the fridge for 30 minutes or till chocolate is set.

④ Remove the banana splits from cases, pipe squirty cream on top then pop on a glacé cherry. Yum!

68

Marshmallow Manicure!

You'll need:

- Marshmallows
- Food colouring
- Water
- Chocolate finger (like Cadbury Fudge)
- Cocktail sticks
- Greaseproof paper
- Clean paint brush

1. Place greaseproof paper down to protect work surfaces from the food colouring. Put a little drop of water in a small bowl and add food colouring till you get the colour you want.

Make the marshmallow your BF's favourite colour — she'll ♥ it!

2. Use a paintbrush to apply the dye to the marshmallows — dab on a little dye at a time so they don't go gooey. Leave to dry.

3. Cut chocolate sticks into 2cm-long slices. Put a cocktail stick in the centre of the marshmallow then skewer the chocolate finger on top. Enjoy!

Don't forget to tell your friends there's a cocktail stick inside!

Always ask an adult before using any kitchen equipment.

69

Chloe's Cool Games!

Entertain your sleepover guests with these awesome games!

So Daring!

Find out who's fearless with these dare ideas!

Why not? Write the dares on pieces of paper and pull them out of a hat!

Pretend to be a chicken for 30 seconds.

Put on a blindfold and feed yogurt to the person on your right.

Yodel for 10 seconds.

Stuff marshmallows in your mouth and sing *Twinkle Twinkle Little Star*.

Read out the last text you sent.

Get your friends to make a sandwich with any ingredients they want, and eat it.

Swap an item of clothing with the person on your left.

Hop on one foot for one minute.

Would You Rather?

This fun question game will get you giggling!

Eat cake covered in ketchup
OR
Eat a jam-covered pickled onion

Eat a block of butter
OR
Eat a wheel of cheese

Kiss a jellyfish
OR
Hug a scorpion

Have three legs
OR
Have six ears

Have five hours of homework every day
OR
Never get school holidays again

Predict Your Future!

How to play:

MASH is a quiz that predicts your future!

♥ Write MASH along the top of a piece of paper — it stands for Mansion, Apartment, Shack and House and it predicts which one you'll live in! You can predict other things too!

♥ Think of four things that you would like to predict — such as your job, where you'll live and what type of car you'll drive. Write these as small headings on your paper.

♥ Underneath these headings write down four options. Underneath 'Job', you might write Movie star, Best-selling author, Doctor and Art critic.

♥ Roll a dice to get your prediction number and count through your card, scoring out each option you land on. For example, if you rolled a three, score out the S in MASH.

♥ Continue counting from where you left off till you have one option left in each section. This is your future!

This is what my MASH card looked like!

Here's a **MASH** card to get you started — make your own or photocopy it and hand them out at your party!

M A S H

JOB
- Movie star
- Best-selling author
- Doctor
- Art critic

CITY
- Paris
- London
- Sydney
- New York

CAR
- Rolls Royce
- Audi
- Fiat
- Porsche

PET
- Dog
- Cat
- Rabbit
- Tiger

MASH

JOB
- ○
- ○
- ○
- ○

CITY
- ○
- ○
- ○
- ○

CAR
- ○
- ○
- ○
- ○

PET
- ○
- ○
- ○
- ○

Change the headings and ask the MASH card anything!

Sleepover Fear Fixer

Let Daisy and Emily solve your sleepover troubles...

I've been invited to my first ever sleepover. I'm excited, but I can't help worrying... you see, I still snuggle into my old baby blanket every night before falling asleep. I'm scared my friends will think I'm a baby but I just can't sleep without my blanket.

Daisy says:

I felt just the same at Amy's sleepover. I hid my little bear, Midnight, because I knew that Chloe would tease me dreadfully. But when Emily saw Midnight, she thought he was really cute and didn't think me a baby at all. In fact, she had a teddy all of her own!

You'll probably find that lots of your friends have a comforting toy, teddy or blanket to help them drift off to sleep... it's perfectly normal and nothing to be embarrassed about. Enjoy your sleepover!

My mum says I can have a special birthday sleepover with three of my friends. Trouble is, I have four close friends and I don't want to leave anyone out. Help!

Emily says:

If you can't invite all four of your friends to stay over, then why not plan a different activity where everyone can be involved? Ask Mum if you and your friends can have a fun day together instead of a sleepover — you could plan a picnic in the garden, or a day of dancing and party games! You can offer to help with the party preparations to make things easier for your mum.

I desperately want to have my friends over to stay but I'm worried about what they'll think when they see the bedroom I share with my younger sister. The walls are decorated with fluffy bunnies and the floor is always covered in toys because my sister is so messy! What should I do?

Daisy says:

Transform your bedroom into a slumber party den! Start by tidying up and putting everything back in its place. You could drape fairy lights over your headboard, scatter comfy cushions and blankets on the floor, and set out bowls of tasty treats and nibbles. Your friends will be so impressed and distracted by your amazing decorations, they'll barely even notice the wallpaper!

10 reasons why ...

We ♥ sleepovers!

Secrets
Confessing our cringes = lots of giggles!

Late–night stories
Telling spooky tales gives us the shivers.

Eating (lots and lots!)
Nothing beats a midnight feast — yum!

Exciting games
Truth or dare is definitely our fave.

Painting nails
Mini makeovers are so much fun.

Oversleep
Sleeping till late the next morning is a must!

VIP party!
Dressing up and dancing makes us feel fabulous.

Everyone together
Being with our friends is the best.

Relaxing
Chilling and chatting in our onesies — bliss!

Snuggling
Comfy and cosy, we finally slip off to sleep. Zzz...

Make These
SLEEPY KOALA INVITES

YOU'LL NEED:
- Card
- Coloured paper or felt
- Ribbon
- Scissors
- Glue
- Sellotape

Your friends will love these adorable sleepover invites!

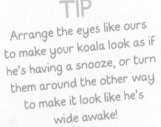

You're Invited!

Where: My bedroom

When: Next Saturday at 7pm

Bring: Your pyjamas and a sleeping bag!

To Tracy's Sleepover!

1 Trace round our party mask shape at the bottom of the page to get a template, then cut it out and glue onto card. Now you can decorate your mask with paper or felt!

TIP
Try creating different kinds of animals. You could make a cute cat with big green eyes or anything you fancy!

2 Cut three round shapes from black felt for the nose and ears. For the eyes, cut out two curvy c-shaped lines. Arrange the features on the mask and stick them down when you're happy with them.

TIP
Arrange the eyes like ours to make your koala look as if he's having a snooze, or turn them around the other way to make it look like he's wide awake!

3 Now attach a pretty ribbon to either side of your mask with sticky tape. Make sure it's long enough to tie around someone's head.

4 Stick the details of your event on the back of your mask. You need to include what the event is, as well as the time, location and what people need to bring!

Template to trace

Jacky talks about...
Fashion & Style

I'm very interested in current fashion and hairstyles — but I often don't like what I see! I think it's a bit boring when everyone tries to look the same. It's much better to develop your own style and be unique. You don't have to spend too much money either — you can often find fantastic bargains in charity shops.

My favourite outfit is currently black jeans, a pretty shirt and an embroidered waistcoat.

I love various fashion designers — long ago I loved Celia Birtwell and now her designs are popular again. She has produced wonderful prints for stores such as Topshop, Uniqlo and Boots.

Photos by Trish Beswick

Did You Know?

Celia Birtwell became famous in the 60s and 70s for designing beautiful floral fabrics. She worked with her fashion designer husband, Ossie Clark, who made them into gorgeous dresses and shirts. Their designs were loved by celebrities and pop stars like The Rolling Stones. Celia was only 13 when she won a place to study at art school.

Describe your favourite outfit here—

My Style Favourites!

Take a peek inside Jacky's wardrobe!

Photos by Trish Beswick

Something I Love...
This is my favourite outfit — I love the embroidery on the waistcoat.

Something Posh...
This is my only sparkly evening dress. I look like a glitter ball when I'm wearing it!

I ♥ Shoes!
My favourite shoes are all black and silver!

Something I Can Wear Every Day...
These are my Celia Birtwell print t-shirts from Uniqlo.

Something New...
This is my new faux fur winter coat. I think I'm going to be very cosy.

Something I Can't Bear to Part With...
I bought this wonderful Alice In Wonderland appliqué jacket thirty years ago in Camden Market.

A Favourite Bag...
I have to be very organised to fit everything into my little handbag.

A Fashion Fabulous Gift...
My lovely Jacob sweatshirt was specially made for me by my friend Trish.

Jacky's Jewels!
There's always a clutter of jewellery on my dressing table.

Ellie's Fashion Mood Board

A mood board is a type of collage that includes pictures and words. Your mood board should be centred round one theme — your theme can be anything, such as homework, craft ideas or fashion!

Totally transform your style!

You can make any mood board you like — it's really useful when studying for exams!

Blank Canvas

Start with a large piece of paper — this is the mood board that you'll put your fashion fabulous pieces on. You can use brightly coloured card, plain paper or if you're feeling up to it, you can pin everything on to a corkboard!

Pick A Theme

Your mood board should have a theme. You could make it pretty and pastel, choose holiday outfits or focus on one item such as jewellery. I've made a Winter Woollies mood board so I can be inspired to look great on freezing cold mornings!

Create a friendship mood board containing pictures of you and your BF — it's a fab present!

Research

You need lots of pictures to put on your mood board. Flip through magazines, print pictures from the internet or draw your own fashion creations.

Use a cork board or letter board and pin on your pictures — then you can change it as often as you like!

My party style!

Make It!

YOU'LL NEED:
- Scissors
- Glue
- Felt–tip pens

Now it's time to piece your mood board together. Begin by sorting through your pictures and picking out your favourites. Place the pictures on your blank canvas and arrange them the way you want — it helps to put your bigger pictures on first. When you're happy with the layout, glue on your pictures, then use felt–tip pens to write on inspiring words and phrases. If you're feeling super–creative, you can add gems, sequins and any little inspiring items you have lying around!

Theme Finder!

Discover **your** fashion trend!

START

I ♥ JACKY'S JEWELLERY

I'M QUITE SHY

SCHOOL DISCOS ARE GREAT

I HAVE A FEW CLOSE FRIENDS

PINK'S MY FAVOURITE COLOUR

I DESIGN MY OWN CLOTHES

SPARKLY SHOWSTOPPERS!
You're loud, proud and love to party. Why not make a party spectacular mood board with lots of sequinned dresses and sparkly jewellery?

COSY & COOL!
You're chilled out and like staying in with a good book. Why not design a mood board full of cosy clothes and funky accessories?

Sapphire's Vintage Treasures

Re-use and recycle just like Sapphire to create amazing accessories!

They're much nicer than Mrs Briskett's!

Key Necklace

You'll need:

- Old keys
- Selection of nail polish
- Embroidery thread
- Gems
- Ribbon, lace or old chain

① Paint your key with some pretty polish and leave to dry.
② Add some gems or glitter and finish with a clear polish top coat.
③ Make a little tassel from thread and tie it to the key.
④ Tie on a ribbon and it's ready to wear!

How to make the tassel:

① Wrap some embroidery thread round two fingers to make a loop.
② Wrap some more thread tightly round the top and trim the bottom of the tassel.
③ Pop a piece of thread through the top loop to tie on.

Why not?

Send one as a Valentine — the key to your heart! Or make a matching necklace for your bestie!

'Sadly there was no food. Mrs Briskett kept all her edible supplies in the larder, and she locked it up each night with the key she kept round her neck.'

Button Accessories

These would look adorable in my fiery red hair.

You'll need:

- Old buttons
- Ponytail bands
- Hair grips

So fast, so pretty!

- Slide a button on to a grip and pin up your hair.

- Thread hair bobbles through button holes like this —

'I did not care for either of their outfits, but I hung my head miserably all the same. I did not even have a bonnet, and had to cover my hair with my borrowed shawl.'

Lace Pom-pom Brooch

'It was wonderful, though, to parade into and out of church in my new green frock with its gold trimmings. I saw some of the younger maids giving it the eye, and I was sure they were looking envious.'

I would wear this with my Sunday best.

You'll need:

- Card
- Lace
- Ribbon
- Safety pin

1 Cut two circles from card.

2 Wrap the lace round and round the circles until the centre hole is filled up.

3 Cut through the lace round the edge and carefully pull apart the two circles.

4 Tightly tie some ribbon lengths between the circles. Remove the card completely and fluff up the pompom.

5 Trim the ribbon ends and use the pin to attach the brooch. Lovely!

Easy-peasy Nail Art!

Follow our step-by-step instructions for the cutest nails ever!

Cute Cupcakes!

You'll need:

- ☆ Nail polish in clear, white, a pastel colour, red and green
- ☆ A hair grip
- ☆ A paper plate
- ☆ A cocktail stick

1 Paint your nails with clear nail polish, then apply two coats of your pastel shade. Two thin coats are better than one thick coat!

2 Use a hair grip to dot white nail polish on to your nail like this.

3

Now use the brush from your white nail polish to sweep the colour to the top of your nail — this will be the cake frosting!

4

On the paper plate, mix a few drops of your pastel nail polish with one drop of white nail polish and use the cocktail stick to stripe it on to your nail like this.

5

Using your hair grip again, dot red nail polish on to the top of your nail for a cherry, then add a streak of white with your cocktail stick to add a shine mark. Use the cocktail stick again to add a stripe of green for the stalk. Finish with a clear top coat and repeat for the rest of your nails!

Pretty Pink Paw Prints!

Try this quick and easy look!

1 Paint your nails using your favourite colour and leave to dry. Now use a hair grip to add a dot of a contrasting colour.

2 Add three smaller dots next to the big dot using a cocktail stick.

3 Repeat all over your nails for a cute paw print look!

Why not try painting a mini me on your thumb nail?!

Ring Design Challenge!

Be bold and unique with your design!

Do you love jewellery as much as Jacky? If you could design your own fabulous ring what would it be like? Draw your design below!

Will your design be big and bold like Jacky's rings or more delicate with thin twists wrapping round your finger?

What gems will you have? Precious stones like emeralds, rubies and diamonds or something more unusual like topaz, morganite or tiger's eye?

Will you choose an animal — a little cat or frog with glowing gemstone eyes?

Will it be made from precious silver or gold? What about rainbow-coloured titanium?

It could be a mystical fairy or sparkling unicorn!

Perhaps you'll choose a theme like sweets, flowers or sea creatures.

Jacky talks about...
Wishes, Dreams and Fears

When I was young I always wished for four things: I wanted to be a writer, I wanted a best friend, I wanted a boyfriend and I wanted to have long fair hair. Well, I never managed the long hair, but I had various boyfriends, I found several wonderful best friends, and I've been a writer all my adult life. Three out of four wishes isn't bad going!

I was very shy as a child and scared of meeting new people and could never think of anything to say. But now I meet new people every day and I find I'm chatting away without even thinking about it. Don't worry if you're shy too, or you find it difficult to make friends, or you wish your home life was different. When you grow up you'll have the chance to make all your dreams come true, I promise you.

No one ever thought I'd make it as a writer — but I managed it all the same. I just needed a tiny bit of talent, hard work and determination, and a lot of luck.

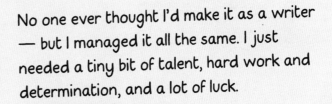

Write your top three wishes here

Me with the books I've written!

1. ....

2. ....

3. ....

I'm crossing my fingers and wishing very hard that all your dreams come true too.

Discover Your Destiny!

What does the crystal ball hold for you?

Your personality can reveal your future!

1. What job have you always dreamed of doing?

A. Something that involves travel.

B. Something that will make you rich!

C. Something that's creative.

D. Something that doesn't feel like work!

2. What animal is most like you?

A. A sparkly unicorn.

B. A bouncy kangaroo.

C. An exotic tiger.

D. A hardworking horse.

3. What do you love doing the most?

A. Drawing, painting and customising your clothes.

B. Learning new stuff — about anything, really!

C. You just love to have fun!

D. Visiting new places with your family.

4. Which of these is the most important to you?

A. Being happy in whatever you do.

B. Seeing the Eiffel Tower and the Great Wall of China.

C. Being successful and having your own office.

D. Being a writer or artist, like Jacky and Nick.

5. Now pick which JW character you're most drawn to...

A. Violet (*Midnight*)

B. Floss (*Candyfloss*)

C. Verity (*The Cat Mummy*)

D. Elsa (*The Bed And Breakfast Star*)

Scores:

1) a) 1 b) 2 c) 3 d) 4
2) a) 3 b) 4 c) 1 d) 2
3) a) 3 b) 2 c) 4 d) 1
4) a) 4 b) 1 c) 2 d) 3
5) a) 3 b) 1 c) 2 d) 4

Between 5 and 8

You love going on holiday and visiting new towns and cities, so the crystal ball definitely sees you travelling the world!

Between 9 and 12

You knuckle down and work really hard at anything you put your mind to, so you're likely to be really successful in your job in the future!

Between 13 and 16

You're arty and you love to express yourself, so you'll definitely end up in a creative career. You might even be a famous fashion designer!

Between 17 and 20

You're a free spirit and don't like to make plans. You're not sure what you'd do in the future yet, but it'll definitely be a big adventure!

Now take a pencil and spin it in the centre of the page THREE times to find out your mystic message...

You're feisty and fun — don't let anything stand in your way.

You're very hardworking and driven! Go you!

You're an independent spirit. You'll follow your own path.

You make your own luck. You'll have lots of adventures!

You're a kind, caring person — your family is very important to you.

You'll succeed at anything you turn your hand to. A* for effort!

Your positivity means that all your wishes will come true!

You're fearless! Travel will be a big part of your future.

You're a people pleaser. Don't forget about yourself...

You're a daydreamer. Turn your dreams into reality!

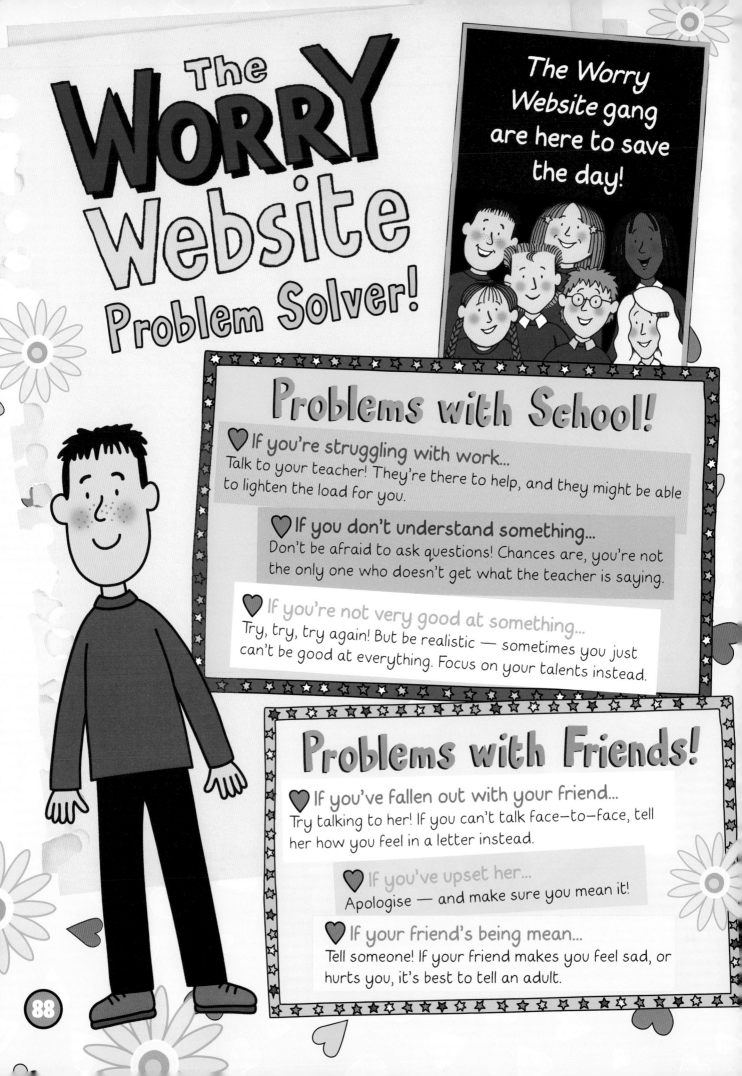

The WORRY Website Problem Solver!

The Worry Website gang are here to save the day!

Problems with School!

♥ **If you're struggling with work...**
Talk to your teacher! They're there to help, and they might be able to lighten the load for you.

♥ **If you don't understand something...**
Don't be afraid to ask questions! Chances are, you're not the only one who doesn't get what the teacher is saying.

♥ **If you're not very good at something...**
Try, try, try again! But be realistic — sometimes you just can't be good at everything. Focus on your talents instead.

Problems with Friends!

♥ **If you've fallen out with your friend...**
Try talking to her! If you can't talk face-to-face, tell her how you feel in a letter instead.

♥ **If you've upset her...**
Apologise — and make sure you mean it!

♥ **If your friend's being mean...**
Tell someone! If your friend makes you feel sad, or hurts you, it's best to tell an adult.

Problems with Bullies!

♥ **If someone makes fun of you...**
Try to laugh it off if it's a one-off — but if it continues, tell an adult you trust.

♥ **If you feel scared by someone...**
You must tell a trusted adult — no one should make you feel worried like this.

♥ **If someone is physically hurting you...**
Tell a teacher or parent. They'll be able to sort out the situation by helping the bully see their behaviour isn't appropriate.

Problems at Home!

♥ **If your parents are splitting up...**
Don't think it's your fault! Parents split up for a number of reasons, but none of them are you.

♥ **If you think your sibling is getting more attention than you...**
It's maybe because they need it! Your parents probably think you're super-mature and don't need so much hands-on attention.

♥ **If you and your siblings are always fighting...**
Try to see things from their point of view — then try to talk it out at a time when you're both calm.

What Your Dreams Mean!

Your dreams often reveal what's bothering you in real life!

Your teeth falling out...

This usually means you're scared of making a fool of yourself in public. It might be that you're quite shy and don't like being the centre of attention. Dreaming about teeth can also represent money — this is linked to the tooth fairy replacing your baby teeth with money. Ooh!

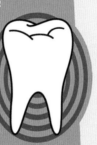

Failing a test...

This could mean that you feel unprepared for some sort of challenge or task ahead — it doesn't necessarily mean an exam. Or it could mean you're worried about being judged by other people and maybe not living up to their expectations. You care what other people think too much!

Being naked...

Aaargh! Ever woken up in a cold sweat after this one? Well, it's another common dream — it could mean that you're worried about being yourself in a situation. If no one bats an eyelid about your lack of clothes in your dream then, hooray, it means you're worrying over nothing!

Flying...

If you're having a blast and zipping about all over the place then you're feeling super-confident. You can do anything! If you're having difficulty staying in the air, something in your life is preventing you doing everything you want to do. Time to work out what that is. Oo-er...

You're being chased...

This suggests you sometimes run away from your problems rather than face them head on — you bury your head in the sand and try to carry on as normal! If the chaser is gaining on you then it means your problem will catch up with you eventually — it's time to take a deep breath and face it!

A celebrity...

You enjoy being the centre of attention and want people to recognise your talents. You want to get noticed, just like a celeb!

Fog...

You dream of fog when something is unclear in your life. It could be that you're confused about something and can't see clearly...

Spiders...

Dreaming of spiders could simply mean that you're scared of them. But they could represent something else you're scared or worried about!

Telephone...

You want to say something to somebody but don't feel that you can for some reason — maybe you don't want to hurt their feelings!

Water...

If the water is a calm, placid lake it means you're happy and peaceful. Rough waves mean you're troubled by something!

If You Met...
The Psammead...

What would you wish for?

Tick one thing from each section —

You might ask for unlimited wishes!

Your Wishes
What's your number one wish?
- [ ] Go on the holiday of your dreams
- [ ] Meet Jacqueline Wilson
- [ ] Become a best-selling author
- [ ] Be an Artist Extraordinaire like Nick
- [ ] Pass all your exams

Caring Wishes
Give back to the world with a caring wish!
- [ ] Stop animal cruelty
- [ ] Be able to communicate with animals
- [ ] Have all the pets you want

92